The Great
PESACH
FUNBOOK

Don't PASS OVER this one!

Can you find me in this book? Good luck!

By *Chani Saposh*

judaica
PRESS

Contents

ISBN: 978-1-60763-148-4

THE JUDAICA PRESS, INC.
123 Ditmas Avenue
Brooklyn, NY 11218
718-972-6200
info@judaicapress.com
www.judaicapress.com

CHANI SAPOSH is the editor of the monthly children's publication *Itonli*, which has been published in Israel for over twenty years. She is a top-level graphic artist as well as a multi-published author who has developed, written, and designed a wide variety of reading books and educational pamphlets for children, some of which that have been incorporated into the framework of school curriculums throughout Israel. She also partners with others in the planning and design children's games. One of Chani's specialties is creating recreational material that is both fun and educational for a variety of ages, for home and school use.

Chani can be reached at lhs@012.net.il

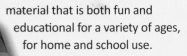

Manufactured in China

Singing!

The Pesach Haggadah is filled with songs that we love to sing all Pesach long. All the children on this page have a song to sing; each one is singing one song. We have to guess which song it is.

Listen to the part of the song each one is singing, and think.

How does the song begin? Fill in the blank with the first words of each song ...

Sheb
Sheb'chol halaylos

BiY
BiYerushalayim

Karpas
Karpas, Yachatz

Dai
Dai, Daiyeinu

V'asa
V'asa shunra

La
La'avoseinu v'lanu

echad
Echad ani yodei'a!

The Matzah Bakery Game

18-Minute Matzah

We're going to bake matzahs for Pesach!
Every player in this game is an energetic baker, rushing to finish baking his matzahs in the shortest time possible. Hurry — before the dough can turn into chometz!

Directions: To play this game, remove these two pages and tape them together. Add one die, and use a game piece for each player.

Start the game at the well, where the players are drawing water to use for the matzah dough.

Roll the die. Move your game piece the number of spaces that is on the die. The winner is the first one to get to the freshly baked matzahs coming out of the oven!

Shemurah Flour for Pesach

The matzah hasn't been pricked with holes – the dough may rise up!

Baking

Wait 2 turns while the matzah bakes

The **FINISHED MATZAH!**

Go back to the Making Holes space

END

Putting the matzah into the oven

The matzah has folded over! It could become chometz!

This matzah is really thick. Go back and roll it at the Rolling Station.

Making Holes in the matzah

Go back to START

Time is running out! Move ahead 4 spaces.

Rolling Station Rolling out the matzah dough

The dough is not kneaded enough! Go back to Kneading and knead it some more.

Advance to the Matzah Dough Rolling station

Kneading

Flour

Hurry! Go forward 2 spaces

The table had Chometz on it! Clean it and go back to **START**

Measuring & mixing

The Outsider

Take a look at every line: 3 out of the 4 items have something in common. But one item does not belong with the others! Circle that item.

Wanted: Illustrator!

The illustrator did not complete all the pictures for the new Haggadah. There are still four missing pictures ... Can you help him out and fill in the missing pictures? Before you begin drawing, stop and think for a minute. How do you think the wise son should look? The wicked son? And the other sons? Take a pencil, an eraser and your markers and fill in the empty boxes here.

רשע

The wicked son

חכם

The wise son

ואינו יודע לשאול...

The one who does not know how to ask

תם

The simple son

Benny Is Confused!

Benny is confused. When did the Red Sea split? What's the difference between *Maror* and *Charoses*? When is the first night of Pesach? What is ...? Can you help Benny answer all of his questions?

Seder night is:

A. In the Land of Israel, the first night of Pesach, or outside the Land of Israel, the first two nights.

B. The last night of Pesach.

C. The same night as *bedikas chometz*, the night we check for *chometz* all over our house.

On the same night as Seder night, over 3000 years ago ...

D. The Sea split.

E. We were allowed to leave Egypt.

F. We received the Torah at Mount Sinai.

Charoses is ...

G. One of the songs we sing from the Haggadah.

H. A sweet, mushy food that we dip the maror into, to remind us of cement.

I. The name of a special sweet fruit that used to grow in Egypt.

The Seder Plate (the K'arah) has on it ...

J. Charoses, gefilte fish, chrain, kugel, and salt water.

K. A shankbone (Zeroah), an egg, maror, charoset, karpas, and chazeres.

L. An egg, salt water, maror, a Purim cookie and a latke.

B	F	C	X	R	T	Y	U	I	O	L	G	S
S	A	E	H	F	P	A	H	G	M	E	A	B
C	H	V	K	N	M	Z	W	Q	K	R	T	Y
X	K	M	P	C	A	K	M	J	P	H	M	G
Z	P	I	B	S	E	D	o	Y	W	Q	E	F
Y	M	F	G	B	H	P	A	X	H	P	K	X
N	Q	W	S	D	G	J	L	U	Y	T	V	C

On Seder night we drink ...

M. Four cups of wine or grape juice, like the four expressions of redemption.

N. Just from the cup of Eliyahu HaNavi (Elijah the Prophet).

O. As much wine as we want to, until the Seder is over.

On the second night of Pesach, we start counting...

P. Sefiras HaOmer, the countdown until the holiday of Shavuos.

Q. The minutes until Eliyahu Hanavi will come and drink his cup of wine.

R. How many days are left of Pesach vacation until we have to go back to school.

How will we know if Alex picked all the right answers?

Take a look again — next to every answer there is a letter. Find the letters that appeared next to the answers you chose in the puzzle below and color them in. If you really helped Benny find all the right answers, you will now see what is written in the puzzle! Happy coloring!

T	S	D	F	G	U	I	O	J	G	F	X	Z
Q	A	E	H	C	E	A	K	W	P	L	A	S
W	P	F	K	F	H	X	C	B	K	J	M	D
D	K	A	M	B	K	O	J	V	M	P	E	L
G	H	I	P	S	P	F	B	S	H	C	K	B
Y	E	R	A	L	M	A	P	Y	E	W	H	X
S	D	T	B	C	B	V	X	G	R	Q	J	Y

The 10 Plagues

Here are all the ten plagues but ... oh no! They are totally out of order! Which one should come first? Which one is second? And then?

It's up to you to sort out this jumble — Put numbers in the circle on top of each plague, from 1–10 , in the order that they really happened.

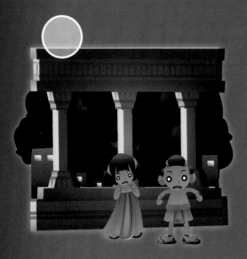

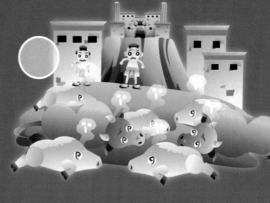

What Did I Get for Afikomen?

Binny, Shmulie, Rikki and Devorah all took the Afikomen at their Seder. What did they ask for as a present for returning it? Trace each one to his or her present; use a different color pen for each one and see what they got!

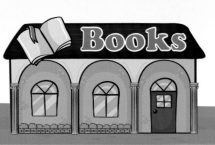

Which Store?

In honor of Pesach we did lots of shopping in many different stores. Which stores did we visit?
Draw a line from every item to the store it came from. Look at the previous page, too — from which store did everyone get their present? Draw a line from each present to the matching store.

The Pesach Crossword

How much do you know about Pesach? Let's find out!
Fill in the answers to these questions on the right-hand page:

1. The half-piece of matzah that we put away at the beginning of the Seder is ...

2. What we do not eat on Pesach

3. The name for the first night of Pesach (Hint: It can also be the name for the second night of Pesach!)

4. The food that looks like cement

5. The name of the book that we read together during the Sedarim

6. The land where we worked as slaves

7. The name of the river in Egypt

8. The third plague

9. Ten _____ that Hashem brought upon the Egyptians

10. Yocheved and Miriam were ... (their job)

11. We open the door during the Sedarim for ...

12. The "bread" we eat on Pesach

13. The leader who led the Jews out of Egypt

14. The part of the Seder during which we eat the Afikomen

Did you finish the whole crossword? Great!

I'm sure you noticed that one line is colored in yellow.
Read this line from the top to bottom and see what it says ... It's something special we put on the Seder table!

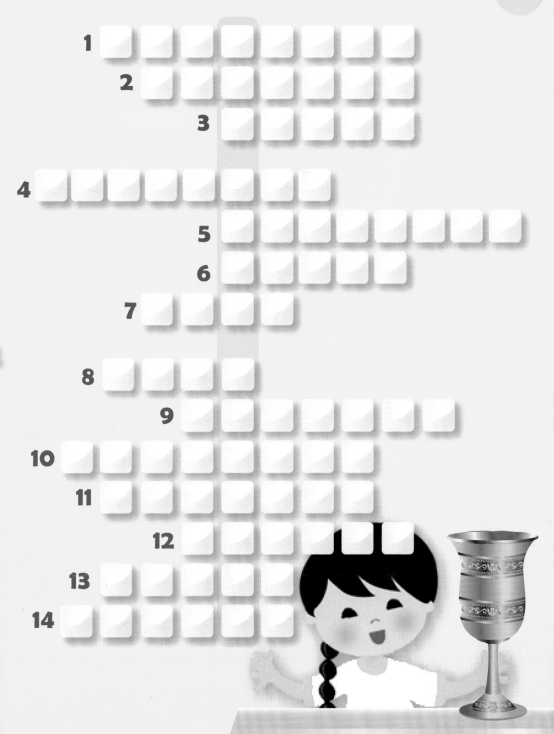

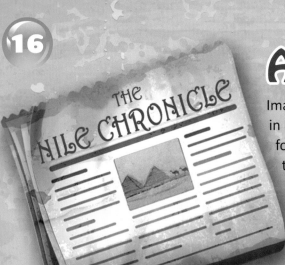

Ancient News

Imagine that there were newspapers in Egypt way back then ... and imagine for a minute that we actually found these newspapers and could read the news written in them from more than 3,000 years ago ... Now take a look below — here are a few articles from an ancient Egyptian newspaper! Read the articles. They are written in newspaper style, which sounds much different than how we read it in the Torah. Can you figure out which event each article is referring to?

Defeat at the Sea of Reeds

From the direction of the desert, reports have been coming in about a terrible event that happened at the Sea of Reeds. All our soldiers, armies and battalions have drowned in the sea. It's difficult to understand what possessed our captains to charge, together with their horses and chariots, directly into the churning sea. Nomads who witnessed what happened have reported that when the armies charged in, the area was dry. Once they were inside, the sea suddenly returned and they were unable to get out. It bears mentioning that not even one soldier who ran after the escaping Jews has returned as of yet. As each hour passes with no other news, the future of the Egyptian army seems uncertain.

Can you guess what event this is?

A National Disaster

Yesterday, all of Egypt's water supplies turned to blood. Our news bulletins say that the stench coming from the Nile River is just incredible. Even the water that people have drawn from wells and stored in their houses has been reported deep red. The thirst is overwhelming. We have no idea what the Jewish slaves did, but they still have pure water.

Can you guess what event this is?

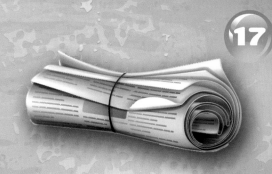

The Sorcerer's Fiasco

Latest news flash from Pharaoh's palace: Pharaoh is seriously thinking about firing his sorcerers, due to their inability to create lice. The leader of the Jewish slaves managed to turn all the dust of Egypt into lice, while Pharaoh's sorcerers could not. Pharaoh is attempting to discover how this Jew got his special magical skills.

Can you guess what event this is?

Animal Attack!

Wild animals are on the loose all over Egypt and they are tearing apart everything in their path. Even though the zoo is locked, lions, tigers and other wild animals are roaming the streets of the city. We could not get a statement from the king's minister about this, as he was being attacked by a wild bear.

Can you guess what event this is?

A Day of Rest

The slaves' union has proposed an unusual idea. Their leader entered the King's palace and demanded that they be given one day a week as a rest day. The slaves' union leader asserts that this will enable the slaves to work more efficiently. Against all odds, Pharaoh actually agreed to their request! From now on, there will be improvement in the working conditions of all slaves; their workweek will consist of six days only.

Can you guess what event this is?

Treasure Hunt

People have been finding treasures hidden in the Egyptian pyramids.
Do you also want to find a treasure?

	Camel	3J
	Snake	5G
	Stone	3N, 7P
	Palm tree	5U
	Pyramid	5P
	River	10-L,M,N,O,P
	Hill	4G

Start at the square under the two date palms (marked with an X)

See the compass on the lower right for the directions.
Go South 3 squares. Continue East to the hill, and then South to the snake. Walk East 3 squares, and then North to the camel. Go East to the stone, and then South to the river. Walk East along the river, and then North to the other stone. Continue to the pyramid and then go East to the palm tree.

Here is a picture of a desert and pyramids. Add in illustrations according to the secret note you'll find in the ancient scroll that is on the far left. Then use the directions that follow to draw the path to the treasure.

Did you finish? Now take a look at the path you drew. You traveled over several letters. Put these letters into the treasure chest in the same order that you walked on them, and then try to read what is written on the box — this is what is waiting for you in the chest of treasures!

Who Knows Four?

FOUR is a central theme all throughout Pesach. During the Sedarim we drink FOUR cups of wine, we have FOUR words of redemption, the youngest child asks FOUR questions, we have FOUR sons, and more.

From the list on the right, try to find the bolded words in this puzzle below. The words appear from left to right, right to left, up and down, or down and up. There are no words on a diagonal line.

Puzzle grid:

```
B D Y F
A O N S
N E O A
O S S R
I N E A                      T N L A
T O L H                      F B E M
P T P S                      O V H B
M K M G                      U P C A
E N I W F O S P U C R U O F H
D O S H O L I D A Y Q A R R A
E W H P M A T Z O S U S B E E
R I V K A H H C A S E P A E L
                             S K D D
                             T L E O
                             I F K M
                             O G C H
                             N A I S
                           E S I W D Y
                           B K A S T A
                           S P R I N G
```

Four Cups of Wine

The **Four Questions**

The Four Sons:
    The **wise** son
    The **wicked** son
    The **simple son**
    The son who **does not know** enough to ask

The Four Names of the Holiday:
    Holiday of **Pesach**
    Holiday of **Freedom**
    Holiday of **Spring**
    Holiday of **Matzos**

The Four Mothers:
    Sarah
    ✓ **Rivkah**
    Rochel
    Leah

The four expressions of **Redemption**

CHALLENGE: Look for a word that appears in the list above more than one time, and try to find it in the word search puzzle. (Hint: It has 7 letters.)

Toothpick Riddle
#1

Everyone is busy cleaning the house for Pesach. Take four toothpicks and create a small "dustpan" on your table, and put a small crumpled piece of paper in the dustpan, as shown below.

Can you move only two toothpicks, in a way that you will have a whole dustpan, while the "garbage" will be outside of it — all without touching the garbage?

Good luck!

What Is Different?

The work in Egypt was so incredibly hard!
There are 10 differences between the 2 pictures. Can you find them? Go ahead and try! To make it more challenging, see if you can do it in 5 minutes or less. Set a timer; now — get ready, get set, and go!

Don't PASS OVER Your Match!

Preparing the Game …
Remove these pages (with the card game) and cut out the cards. We recommend that you save the instructions with the cards, for future use.

Setting Up the Game …
Stack the cards face up in the center. Each player takes one card and places it face down. Note: For each turn, just the top card in the center deck is being played.

Don't PASS OVER your match!	Don't PASS OVER your match!	Don't PASS OVER your match!
Don't PASS OVER your match!	Don't PASS OVER your match!	Don't PASS OVER your match!
Don't PASS OVER your match!	Don't PASS OVER your match!	Don't PASS OVER your match!

Playing the game

The players turn over their cards. Each card shows 5 items. Each player sees if his card has an item that is identical to an item on the center card. The first player to find a matching item announces the name of the item (example: Matzah!) and takes the card from the top of the center stack and puts it on top of his matching card.

Now the center card has been changed. Continue playing the same way. The game is over when there are no more cards in the center pile.

The winner is the player who collects the most cards.

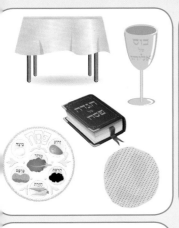

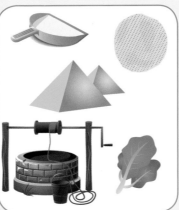

Don't
PASS
OVER
your match!

Don't
PASS
OVER
your match!

Don't
PASS
OVER
your match!

Don't
PASS
OVER
your match!

Don't
PASS
OVER
your match!

Don't
PASS
OVER
your match!

Don't
PASS
OVER
your match!

Don't
PASS
OVER
your match!

Don't
PASS
OVER
your match!

Don't
PASS
OVER
your match!

Don't
PASS
OVER
your match!

Don't
PASS
OVER
your match!

In the Kitchen

Mommy just came home after shopping for Pesach.

Look at the kitchen. Can you find the food that Mommy bought for Seder? Draw a blue circle around all the foods that are especially for the Seder.

Which foods are Chometz? Draw a red circle around those foods that are chometz.

Which foods do we eat on Pesach and during the year as well? Draw a green circle around those foods.

Pesach & Numbers

Pesach has many numbers associated with it.
Do you know what is hinted to by each of these numbers?

10

3

4

8

600

15

49

7

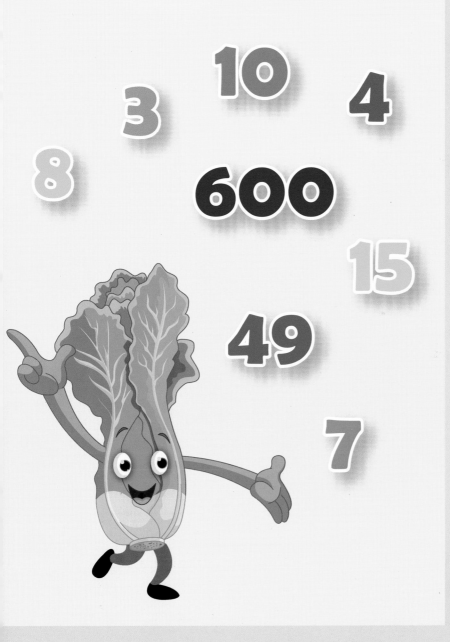

Sudoku

This is a Sudoku game for younger children.

In each square of the Sudoku puzzle there should be 4 items from the Seder night, but some are missing. Can you fill them in?

Cut out the pictures

Sudoku K'arah

A Sudoku for the older kids.

Follow the same directions as the first Sudoku, but each row and column has 6 items.

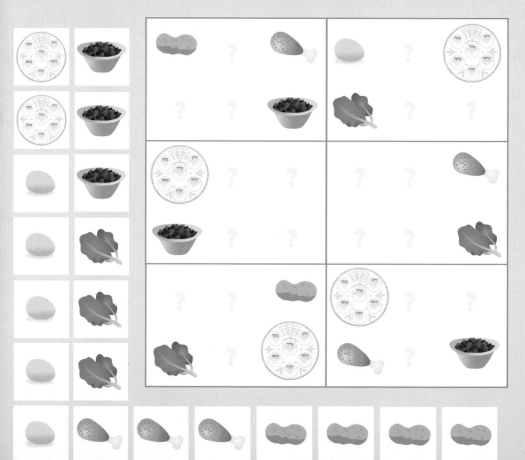

Seder

next to each Sudoku puzzle and place them in the right spot in the puzzle, so that each column and each row should now contain all 4 pictures, with no duplicates.

Enjoy!

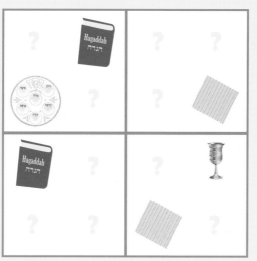

And another Sudoku – This one's a bit harder!

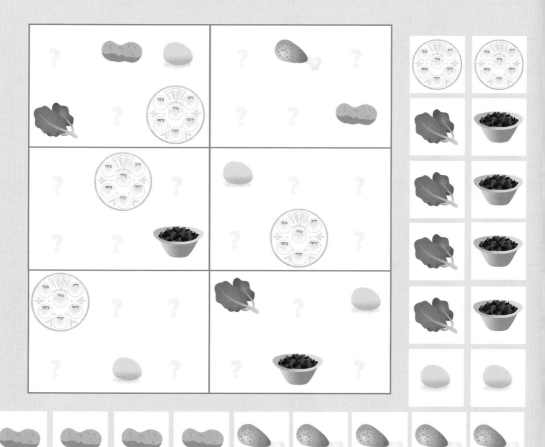

A Family Tale

Do you recognize the picture? Who is the baby in the picture? Where is he? Who put him there? Why?

Who went along with him and hid in the rushes on the side to secretly watch over him?

Did the baby have any brothers or sisters?

What was their father's name? What was their mother's name?

Who took the baby out of the water? What is her father's name?

When she took the baby out of the water, where did she take him?

It's amazing to think about how Hashem planned that the savior of the Jews would grow up in the house of the King of Egypt — the very same king who decreed that all Jewish male babies should be killed, because his astrologists saw that the Jews savior would be born at that time!

When he was three months old, his mother could no longer hide him. She built a cosy little chest and lovingly put

Connect the Dots

Every dot on this board has a name. For example, the first dot on the top left corner is called **"A1"**, because it's in the column of **"A"** and in row "**1**".

Here you have ➡ a list of dots, each with its name. Draw a line between the dots according to the order they are listed here.

- B14 A13 A11 C11 C13 B14 B15 A16 C16 B15
- G6 E6 E9 G9 G12 D12 D5 E4 E1 F1 F4 G5 G9
- M6 M3 J3 J2 N2 N6 M6 M7 L7 L8 H8 H4 L4 L7
- I14 H15 F14 F13 H11 J10 K11 L11 N12 L15 J14 I14 H13 F13
- K11 I14 I15 L16 N13 N12

Note: There are five separate sketches.

Did you find the pictures?

What is their connection to Pesach?

	A	B	C	D	E	F	G	H	I	J	K	L	M	N	
1															
2															1
3															2
4															3
5															4
6															5
7															6
8															7
9															8
10															9
11															10
12															11
13															12
14															13
15															14
16															15
	A	B	C	D	E	F	G	H	I	J	K	L	M	N	16

The Seder Fill-In Puzzle

This is a fantastic puzzle! The words that fit into this puzzle are listed below. Each word in this puzzle is a part of the Seder. I'm sure you know them ... Kadesh, Urchatz, and so on.

Here are some tips to get you started on this puzzle:

The words are listed according to how many letters there are in every word.

As you can see, only one word has 13 letters — this word is already in place for you, and it is already checked off on the list below.

Now look at the letter **"S"** in the word *Shulchan Orech*. This **"S"** is part of another word, that has to be written vertically. That vertical line has space for a word that has 6 letters.

Look at the list of words that have 6 letters and pick out the word that has an "S" for its fifth letter ... Did you find it? Write it in. Now check it off the list.

Now that you've started, you will certainly find all the spaces for all the rest of the words. You'll know the puzzle is correct if every single word fits in!

5 Letters	6 Letters	7 Letters
Maror	Hallel	Bareich
	Kadesh	Nirtzah
	Karpas	Urchatz
13 Letters	Korech	Yachatz
✓ Shulchan Orech	Maggid	
	Matzah	
	Motzei	**8 Letters**
	Tzafun	Rachtzah

ShulchanOrech

Matzah Marshmallow Melt

It's hard to believe that you could use matzah to make something so yummy it could be a dessert!

Serves 2

Here's how you do it!

- Take the butter out of the fridge to soften it about a half hour before you plan to use it.
- Preheat the oven to 350°F (180°C).
- Spread butter on each piece of matzah.
- Line a dairy baking tray with parchment paper and place two of the buttered matzah pieces on it. The buttered size should be facing up.
- Sprinkle 1 cup of mini-marshmallows onto each matzah. They should stick somewhat to the butter. If they do not stick, place them on the matzah pieces one at a time and they will stick. Sprinkle some chocolate chips in between the marshmallows.
- Top each with the other buttered matzah, with the buttered side facing down. Spray the top of your matzah melt with a bit of cooking oil spray.
- Place pan in the oven for about 10 minutes, so that the marshmallows and chocolate chips melt.
- Use a spatula to flatten the matzahs together and then transfer the melts onto two plates.
- Let it cool off a bit first and then enjoy! Just watch out — it's sure to make a sticky, yummy mess!

Let's get to it!

4 square matzahs

4 tablespoons butter

2 cups mini-marshmallows

1 cup chocolate chips

Cooking oil spray

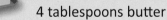

Mock Oatmeal Cookies

Let's get to it!

3/4 cup oil

3 eggs

1 cup matzah meal

1 cup matzah farfel

1 cup sugar

½ teaspoon cinnamon

1 teaspoon baking soda

1/2 cup raisins
+ 1 teaspoon additional matzah meal

1/3 cup chocolate chips

1/2 cup chopped walnuts (not finely ground)

And here's how you do it!

● Preheat the oven to 350°F (180°C).
● Beat the eggs in a mixer. Add the oil and continue beating.
● Add the matzah meal, matzah farfel, sugar, cinnamon and baking soda to the eggs. It should be a thick mixture.
● Sprinkle 1 teaspoon matzah meal on the raisins and then fold the raisins, chocolate chips and nuts into the mixture by hand.
● Line cookie sheets with parchment paper.
● Drop the cookie mixture by teaspoonfuls onto the cookie sheet, or roll them into balls and flatten them slightly after you place them onto the cookie sheet.
● Bake the cookies for 15 minutes or until they are slightly browned on top and bottom.
● These cookies freeze well — that is, if you manage to get any in the freezer before everyone comes and eats them all up …

Makes about 24 cookies

These recipes are excerpted from the Pesach cookbook for kids, *Let My Children Cook!* by Tamar Ansh, filled with easy, yummy, and fun foods the whole family is sure to enjoy!

Hieroglyphics

Dr. Schwartz has just discovered an ancient papyrus. It is filled with Egyptian writing in hieroglyphics.

Can you help him decode it? He really wants to know what it says!

The message must be connected to the Jews leaving Egypt, since the papyrus was discovered only a short distance from the Sea of Reeds.

We've found the code for deciphering the papyrus's message. Just exchange the hieroglyphic letters on the next page for our English letters, according to

the code on page 38.
Then you will be able to read
the message those Egyptians
wrote over 3000 years ago!

Antique – or Fake?

An antique dealer has come to the museum with an old piece of stone in his hands. He claims it is from ancient Egypt. The museum's experts are checking it carefully to see if this is a real antique or not.

Here is a section of the Egyptian drawings from the stone.
Check it carefully — is it really a genuine antique, or is it a fake??

Let's Roll!

Follow the path of the chips: For some of them, the path to the bottom is blocked!

"Roll" the chip down the path as far as it can go, following the white line.

Each chip has a letter on it. Write the letter in the circle where it comes to rest.

Now look at the bottom row: what word was formed?

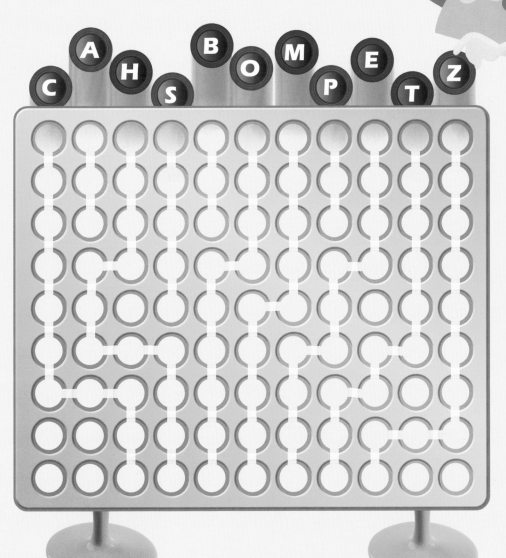

Wine Labels

How about this for a beautiful Seder decoration? See directions on the right.

We drink four cups of grape juice or wine during each of the Pesach Seders. Wouldn't it look special if you made tags for the bottles of wine that will be on your table?

To the left are four different beautiful tags.

Carefully cut this page out of the book, or photocopy it. Then sit down and cut out each tag. When you're done, simply attach each tag to the wine bottles that will be on your table.

Tip: Tags stick best if you attach them to the bottles when they are at room temperature. Bottles that have been in the refrigerator become slightly wet when they are taken out and then you may have trouble getting your tags to stick properly.

Bird's Eye View

Can you identify these pyramids from a bird's eye view? Draw a line connecting each pyramid to its matching sketch on the right. Pay close attention!

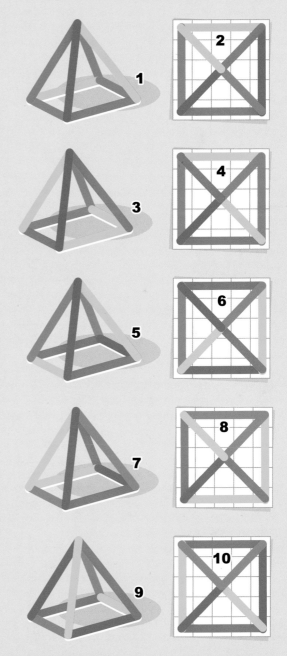

Pesach, Matzah, Maror

Every picture on the left has a matching shadow. Draw a line from each picture to its shadow.

Toothpick Riddle
#2

Take 6 toothpicks and try forming equal triangles. Good luck!

Hint 1:
A similar structure appeared in th book a few times.

Hint 2:
The triangle you see here is part the solution.

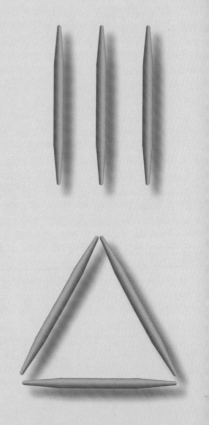

Where Is the Maror?

The entire family is seated at the Seder table and it's time to eat the Maror —
but where did it disappear to? Can you find it in the picture?

Let's Make an Afikomen Bag!

Get yourself a clean, new plastic bag. (It must be clean and new since it will be used for Pesach, and for the Afikomen, no less, so we must ensure it has not even a tiny bit of chometz crumbs in it.) Cut out the sections provided here. Use them to decorate your bag, however you like. You can also add on illustrations or drawings of your own.

Singing! (Page 3)
The songs begin: Mah Nishtanah, L'shanah Haba'ah, Ilu Hotzianu, Kadesh-Urchatz, Chad Gadya, V'hi She'amdah, Echad Mi Yodei'a?

The Outsider (Page 6)
1. Grape soda. 2. Matzah. 3. Pomegranate, which does not belong on the Seder plate. 4. A Purim noisemaker (gragger). 5. A broom, which is not used for Bedikas Chometz.

Alex Is So Confused! (Page 8)
The correct answers are the ones that are near these letters: A, E, H, K, M, P. If you colored these letters in the puzzle below, you should have found the Hebrew name for Passover — **PESACH**.

The 10 Plagues (Page 10)
The correct order of the 10 Plagues is: Blood, Frogs, Lice, Wild Animals, Dead Animals, Boils, Hail, Locusts, Darkness, Plague of the Firstborn.

What Did I Get For Afikomen? (Page 12) A-4, B-1, C-2, D-3.

Which Store? (Page 13)
Fruits & Vegetables Store: peppers, lettuce, carrot; Butcher Store: chicken; Men's Fashion: white shirt, black shoes, belt; Ladies Fashion: red coat, high-heel shoes; Pesach Grocery: matzah, wine, eggs; Fish store: fish; Toy store: dolls, bicycle; Book store: haggadah, siddur; Music store: guitar

The Pesach Crossword (Page 14)
1 Afikomen. 2. Chometz. 3. Seder. 4. Charoses. 5. Haggadah. 6. Egypt. 7. Nile. 8. Lice. 9. Plagues. 10. Midwives. 11. Eliyahu. 12. Matzah. 13. Moshe. 14. Tzafun. Yellow column: "KOS SHEL ELIYAHU"

Ancient News (Page 16)
The incidents mentioned are: Defeat at the Sea of Reeds — The Splitting of the Sea and the Egyptian army drowning in the Sea. A National Disaster — The Plague of Blood. The Sorcerer's Fiasco — The Plague of Lice. A Day of Rest — Pharaoh agreeing to allow the Jews to rest on Shabbos. Animal Attack! — The Plague of Wild Beasts.

Treasure Hunt (Page 18)
If you followed the correct path, you should find the words "**OLD MATZAH**" in the treasure chest.

Who Knows Four? (Page 20)
The challenge word is "HOLIDAY"(highlighted in red)

Toothpick Riddle #1 (Page 21)
The answer is...

What is Different? (Page 22)

Answers

In the Kitchen (Page 27)

The matzahs, lettuce and wine were all bought for the Pesach Sedarim. The bread, pizza, cake, cupcakes, ice cream cones, and pretzels are all chometz. The rest could be either Pesach or year-round foods.

The Afikomen Mystery (Page 28)

Girl C finds the Afikomen.

Pesach & Numbers (Page 29)

10 plagues; 49 days of the Omer; 8 days of Pesach; 4 cups of wine; 600 thousand Jewish men left Egypt; 3 matzahs; Pesach begins on the 15th day of Nissan; The Splitting of the Sea happened on the 7th day of Pesach

Sudoku Seder/Sudoku K'arah

Here are the solutions to the Sudoku:

(Page 30)

(Page 31)

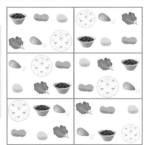

A Family Tale (Page 32)

The picture is of Moshe Rabbeinu as a baby, floating in the little ark on the Nile River. His mother Yocheved put him there so he wouldn't be killed by the Egyptians. Miriam hid in the rushes to watch over him. His sister was Miriam and his brother was Aharon. His father was Amram. Basya, Pharaoh's daughter, took him out of the water and raised him in Pharaoh's palace.

Connect the dots (Page 33)

You should have a picture of a wine bottle and a cup, an open Haggadah and three matzos.

The Seder Fill-In Puzzle (Page 34)

Here are the answers:

Hieroglyphics (Page 38)

The papyrus tells us how the Egyptians were mourning their losses: "Our soldiers drowned in the Reed Sea, and the Jews went free."

Antique – or Fake? (Page 40)

The stone is not genuine — two of the pictures etched into it are of a cellular phone and a bus, both things that were not around at that time!

Let's Roll! (Page 41)

The last row should spell out the word "Chometz."

Bird's Eye View (Page 43)

These are the correct solutions for the pyramids: 1-4, 3-8, 5-10, 7-2, 9-6

Pesach, Matzah, Maror (Page 44)

These are the correct solutions: A-4 , B-1, C-2, D-3.

Toothpick Riddle #2 (Page 44)

The solution: A tetrahedron (a pyramid composed of four triangular faces, one of which is the base), as shown here!

Where is the Maror? (Page 45)

The maror is covering the skirt of the girl in the green sweater.